"Given the explosion of the apostolic movements, *God's Super-Apostles* represents a concise and valuable survey of what is happening around the globe. Geivett and Pivec provide insightful biblical and historical analyses, which are useful for those wanting to understand these sometimes bewildering movements. Especially beneficial are the distinctions the authors make between the teachings of the historic Pentecostal churches and the more recent New Apostolic Reformation views of such leaders as C. Peter Wagner and others."

—**Vinson Synan,** Dean Emeritus, Regent University School of Divinity

"I thank Geivett and Pivec for this book on the New Apostolic Reformation. They will be praised by some and vilified by others for writing it, but one will not, or should not, deny that they have done their work in a careful and professional manner. Here is a plea to compare claims with Scripture in a civil manner, a practice I wholeheartedly commend for all Christians regardless of their theological positions. The apostle Paul commended the Bereans for checking to see if what he was teaching complemented or contradicted the Scripture. If the apostle to the Gentiles commended this action from his hearers in the first century, one would hope that leaders of the NAR movement would see this as a biblical and prudent response to their message in the twenty-first century."

—**Karl I. Payne,** Pastor of Leadership Development and
Discipleship Training, Antioch Bible Church, Redmond, Washington;
Chaplain, Seattle Seahawks

"For centuries the church has cautiously approached identifying apostles and prophets, knowing the enormous potential for abuse that such titles offer. Geivett and Pivec capture this concern, and they rightly affirm that Pentecostals and charismatics may find themselves at particular risk of these ideas. In *God's Super-Apostles*, pastors or sincere followers of Christ can discover a valuable contribution to their need for careful discernment in their understanding of spiritual authority."

—**Mike Clarensau,** Senior Director of Healthy Church Network;
General Council of the Assemblies of God

"The authors clearly and systematically describe the movement's origins and outworkings, and they offer a thoughtful, balanced, and biblical counterpoint to its many errors and excesses. Their work is eminently practical, desperately needed, and long overdue."

—**Paul Carden,** Executive Director,
The Center for Apologetics Research

"I am personally persuaded that, when the history of the ideas of the church at the beginning of the twentieth-first century is written in the future, Geivett's and Pivec's book, *God's Super-Apostles,* will become one of the most essential texts of our time. It is not only an engaging, enlivening, and critical assessment of the New Apostolic Reformation movement (without being uncharitable), but above all, timely and educational for those who want to be faithful to Scripture. A must read for any Latin American who wants to be informed about the growth of the Church of Christ in the Global South."

—**Mario Ramos-Reyes,** Director of the Institute for the Study of
Culture, Ethics, and Development; Visiting Professor at the School of
Law and Philosophy, Catholic University of Paraguay

"If you are looking for a biblically balanced, hermeneutically sound, enlightening, logical, clear, and spiritually and intellectually enriching treatment of the New Apostolic Reformation, contemporary apostles and prophets, their teachings, and the confusions surrounding these, then *God's Super-Apostles* is a must read. It is relevant and much needed globally."

—**Sudhakar Mondithoka,** Director of Hyderabad Institute of
Theology and Apologetics, India

"Like the Bereans, who 'searched the Scriptures daily,' Geivett and Pivec encourage us to look at our church's so-called contemporary apostles and prophets and their movement called New Apostolic Reformation. Although thoroughly researched, the authors give us eye-opening details of these leaders, organizations, and their ideologies in readable English without academic jargon. The result is a very enlightening, very bold, and very cautioning volume. Every Christian must read it."

—**Varghese Thomas,** Hindustan Bible Institute and College, India

"*God's Super-Apostles* is a thorough study and objective view of the New Apostolic Reformation. It is a necessary read for both traditional Pentecostals and those participating in NAR. We have needed this material for a long time."

—**Gary R. Allen,** Former Executive Editor, *Enrichment Journal*; General Council of the Assemblies of God

"Ever since the initial thirst for God, fostered by the Perestroika, faded, believers in the former Soviet Union have been looking for a way to expedite a new powerful awakening. Thus, many saw restoration of the apostolic and prophetic office with its promise of divine empowerment as just the missing piece of the puzzle. Unaware of the intricate history and aberrant doctrinal context of these ideas, many believers were fascinated with the stories of success. Self-proclaimed apostles—both foreign and domestic—multiplied. With their new carefully researched and thoroughly documented book, written in a straightforward yet tactful manner, Geivett and Pivec do a great service to the worldwide Body of Christ by exposing the unorthodox nature of the New Apostolic Reformation, demonstrating its wide influence and putting its teachings and practices in the proper biblical and ethical context."

—**Dmitry Rozet,** Senior Editor, The Center for Apologetics Research

In two recent books, R. Douglas Geivett and Holly Pivec provide a balanced biblical critique of the New Apostolic Reformation.... Both books are well written, fairly argued, and amply documented.... As a classical Pentecostal, I see brothers and sisters among leaders and followers of the New Apostolic Reformation. Chances are, you, your family, or your church has heard of NAR's doctrines or have been influenced by them. With R. Douglas Geivett and Holly Pivec, I believe that NAR doctrines are not true because unbiblical and unhelpful because not true.

—**George P. Wood,** Executive Editor, Assemblies of God Publications; General Council of the Assemblies of God

*God's Super-Apostles* is a clear and winsome work that provides just the right depth of examination, and that comes to clear and biblical conclusions.

—**Tim Challies,** Author and blogger at Challies.com

# STUDY GUIDE FOR
# GOD'S SUPER-APOSTLES

### Encountering the Worldwide
### Prophets and Apostles Movement

*R. Douglas Geivett and Holly Pivec*

Publishing

Baffin Bay Publishing

*Study Guide for God's Super-Apostles: Encountering the Worldwide Prophets and Apostles Movement*
Copyright © 2017 by R. Douglas Geivett and Holly Pivec

Requests for information should be addressed to:
*Baffin Bay Publishing, P.O. Box 10068, Fairbanks, AK 99710*

ISBN 978-1-946541-00-0

Based on the book *God's Super-Apostles: Encountering the Worldwide Prophets and Apostles Movement,* published by Weaver Book Company.

*Cover art: Mark Dobratz*
*Cover design: Frank Gutbrod*

*Printed in the United States of America*

17 18 19 20 21 22 23 24 25 26 27 / 15 14 13 12 11 10 9 8 7 6 5 4 3 2 1

# CONTENTS

# HOW TO USE THE STUDY GUIDE

This study guide will deepen your study of our book *God's Super-Apostles: Encountering the Worldwide Prophets and Apostles Movement*. It can be used for individual or group study. By reading each chapter in the book, and answering the questions in this guide, you'll gain a greater understanding of the New Apostolic Reformation or NAR (pronounced NAHR) than even many of the movement's participants have.

The questions will help you understand what NAR leaders teach about topics like apostles, prophets, spiritual warfare, demons, and miracles. They'll also help you examine what the Bible teaches about these topics. Some questions guide you to reflect on your own experiences with NAR. Others encourage you to develop strategies for responding to its growing influence in your families and churches.

If you're using this guide with a group, we encourage you to first answer the questions on your own. During the discussion, study leaders can decide whether to have their groups answer all the questions. Where time is a limitation, they can pre-select specific questions they believe will best aid discussion. For your convenience, the questions cite page numbers where answers can be found. The page numbers reference the print copy of the book. These can be ignored if working from an e-book version of *God's Super-Apostles*.

May this study guide assist your efforts to be a good Berean, patiently searching the Scriptures to see how NAR lines up (Acts 17:11).

Doug and Holly

# STUDY QUESTIONS

# Preface

1. Why did Doug and Holly write this book?

2. Do all people affiliated with NAR hold to the same beliefs on all points? Why is this significant?

3. Do all classical Pentecostals and charismatics adopt NAR beliefs and practices? Why is this an important question?

4. What other book have Doug and Holly written on the topic of the New Apostolic Reformation? How does that book differ from this one?

5. What thoughts and questions do you have as a result of reading the Preface to *God's Super-Apostles*?

# Chapter 1

# What is the New Apostolic Reformation?

1. Read the three true stories on pages 1-2. How did you feel about the experiences of Mark, Robert, and Jake? What is the common thread in these stories?

2. What do NAR leaders promise those who submit to their leadership? What, according to them, are the risks if you don't submit? (See p. 3.) What does the "corporate spirit of religion" or the "spirit of religion" refer to in C. Peter Wagner's teaching? (See footnote 2 on p. 3.)

3. How many people in the United States today openly embrace the leadership of NAR apostles and prophets? (See p. 3.)

4. Why do NAR leaders call this movement "apostolic"? Why do they consider it a "reformation"? (See p. 4.)

5. Can a person who has never heard of the "New Apostolic Reformation" still be influenced by NAR? How is this possible? (See p. 4.)

6. Read the list of influential apostles, prophets, and NAR teachers (on p. 5). Do you recognize any of these names or organizations? What do you know about them? Are you surprised to see them listed here?

7.  Read the list of NAR organizations and media outlets (on p. 6). Do you recognize any of these organizations? What do you know about them? Are you surprised to see them listed here?

8.  What thoughts and questions do you have as a result of reading this chapter?

# Chapter 2

# NAR Apostles: The Generals

1. What is the central NAR teaching about apostles? Why do Doug and Holly speak of NAR apostles as the "generals" in the NAR movement? How is this linked to the NAR idea that their apostles must "govern" the church today? (See pp. 7-12.)

2.  How has the term "apostle" been used in Protestant Christianity during its history? (See pp. 8-9.) What have Pentecostals and charismatics typically believed about apostles today? (See p. 9.)

3.  How do Doug and Holly use the term Pentecostal in this book? How do they use the term charismatics? (See footnote 1 on p. 9.)

4. Doug and Holly note that the world's largest Pentecostal denomination is the Assemblies of God church. How have leaders of the Assemblies of God church responded to NAR teachings? For the answer to this, visit the various Internet sites listed in footnote 2 on page 9.

5. In the NAR movement, what is the relationship between a local church pastor and an apostle or apostolic network? (See pp. 10-11.) What is the practice of spiritual covering or spiritual protection? What are the benefits and risks related to this practice? (See pp. 11-12.)

6. What are the key New Testament passages used by NAR teachers to support their view of apostles in the church today? (See pp. 12-14.) What is the "fivefold ministry," and what passage is thought to support this doctrine? (See p. 13.) What do you think this passage actually teaches? What does C. Peter Wagner think about the way the church has been governed during most of its history? What does he think 1 Corinthians 12:28 teaches about this? How does he propose to recover the New Testament teaching about church governance? (See p. 14.)

7.  What are NAR apostles expected to do? Which activities are expected of all contemporary apostles? Which are expected of many, but not all, contemporary apostles? (See pp. 14-16.)

8.  Do you know of people who claim to perform any of these functions of a NAR apostle? Are there leaders in your church who make these claims?

9. What is the name of the largest network of NAR apostles in the world today? How extensive is their influence? Do you recognize the names of past members of this coalition? (See pp. 16-17.)

10. Have you ever been called upon to submit to the authority of a NAR apostle or prophet? What does it mean if you do not submit? (See p. 16.) What are your current thoughts and feelings about this?

11. What thoughts and questions do you have as a result of reading this chapter?

# Chapter 3

# Apostles in the Bible: A Close Look

1. This chapter offers a biblical account of apostles and their roles and functions. Doug and Holly distinguish between "apostles of Christ" and "apostles of the churches." Who were the apostles of Christ? Who were apostles of the churches? (See pp. 25-26 and 28.)

2. Who were the twelve apostles, also known as "the Twelve"? Why did Jesus refer to them as apostles? (See p. 18.)

3. What was unique about the role of the Twelve? What did membership in this group of apostles require? Read Acts 1:21-22. What happens in this passage? What does this teach us about the unique role of the Twelve? Based on Acts 10:39-41, what else is true about this unique group of individuals? (See pp. 18-19.)

4. What were the three main functions of the twelve apostles? Study the passages mentioned on pages 19-21 and make a list of truths taught about this group of individuals. Include all the relevant observations you can make.

5. Who was the most influential apostle of the Christian church? Why does he enjoy this distinction? What did he do to show that he was a genuine apostle? What were his apostolic functions? What is the argument that this great apostle was the "last apostle"? (See pp. 21-24.)

6. On pages 24-26, Doug and Holly describe another group of New Testament apostles. Make a list of the New Testament passages that name and describe these apostles. Make a list of the apostles mentioned by name. What do we know about each of these men and women? In what sense are these figures also called "apostles"? How do they differ from the Twelve and from the apostle Paul? (See especially p. 25.)

7. Who are the "false apostles" spoken of in 2 Corinthians 11:13-15? What other passages of the New Testament include warnings about false apostles? What criteria were used by the Ephesian Christians to recognize false apostles in their midst? (See pp. 26-27.)

8. Do you believe there are false apostles in the church today? What criteria would you use to identify them today?

9. Suppose you meet someone who claims to be an apostle. What should you do if you aren't sure whether his or her claim is true? Should you give them the benefit of the doubt and assume that they are an apostle until you have good reason to believe otherwise? Should you be more cautious than that? Should you conclude that they are false apostles?

10. Is there any danger in calling someone a "false apostle"? What if someone really is a false apostle? Will it always be really obvious?

11. What thoughts and questions do you have as a result of reading this chapter?

# Chapter 4

# NAR Apostles vs. Apostles in the Bible

1. What is the major thesis of this chapter? (See p. 29 and p. 41.)

2. What do NAR leaders teach about the governing role of an apostle in the church today? What passages in the New Testament do they use to support their teaching? (See pp. 29-31.)

3. What do NAR leaders teach about Ephesians 4:11-13? How do Doug and Holly reply to this understanding of the passage? What is the NAR teaching about 1 Corinthians 12:28? What do Doug and Holly say about this passage? (See pp. 30-31.)

4. What is the New Testament evidence that "the governing office of apostle was temporary"? (See pp. 31-32.)

5. What is the difference between an apostle with governing authority in a church and an apostle that does not have governing authority? Is this a New Testament concept? Are there apostles in the church today who do not have governing authority? If so, what is their role in the church and the world today? (See pp. 32-33.)

6. Doug and Holly describe five tests for genuine apostleship. What are these tests? Do you agree that these are biblically grounded tests for an apostle? Do you think there are other tests that should be used to evaluate a person's claim to be an apostle? (See pp. 33-41.)

7. Using the five tests, how would you know whether a person today, who claims to be an apostle, is a genuine apostle in the NAR sense? Do you know anyone who claims to be an apostle? Does that person meet all five tests of apostleship?

8. Must an apostle have a track record of performing miracles? C. Peter Wagner and Bill Hamon disagree with each other on this point. How do they differ? What do you think about this requirement? (See pp. 36-37.)

9. Doug and Holly describe the "Wagner test" for determining the divine authority [authenticity] of a NAR revelation claim. What is this test? (See p. 38.) Why is this test inadequate for evaluating any new revelation? (See pp. 38-40.)

10. What is the "Berean principle" for evaluating a new revelation? (See p. 38.) What biblical passage refers to this principle? Read this passage. Doug and Holly describe three criteria for applying the Berean principle. What are these criteria? (See pp. 38-40.) Identify two or three NAR revelation claims. Applying the Berean principle, how do these claims measure up?

11. Do you know anyone who claims to be an apostle with governing authority in the church today? What would such a person say about the five tests of an apostle described by Doug and Holly in this chapter? Do you know anyone today who meets these five tests of an apostle?

12. What thoughts and questions do you have as a result of reading this chapter?

# Chapter 5

# NAR Prophets: The Secret Intelligence Agents

1. How do you feel after reading Caleb's story on page 42? Do you know of a situation similar to Caleb's? Describe what happened in that situation.

2. What is the central NAR teaching about prophets? Why do Doug and Holly speak of NAR prophets as the "secret intelligence agents" in the NAR movement? How is this linked to the NAR idea that they, like the apostles, must "govern" the church today? (See pp. 43-44.)

3. How does the NAR teaching about contemporary prophets differ from the teachings of classical Pentecostals and charismatics? (See pp. 43-44.)

4. What is the doctrine of "cessationism"? What position do Doug and Holly take on this doctrine? (See p. 43, together with the footnote on this page and page ix in the Preface.)

5. What is the relationship between a NAR prophet and a pastor of a local church supposed to be? What do NAR leaders teach about the importance of prophets based on Matthew 10:41 and Psalm 105:15? Do you agree with their use of these passages? How would you support your answer? (See p. 44.)

6. How do NAR leaders defend their teaching about prophets in the church today? What passages of the Bible do they cite? How would you evaluate their use of Amos 3:7? (See p. 47.)

7. Study the list of other things NAR prophets do outside of local churches. Doug and Holly divide these activities and functions into three groups. What are the three groups? What actions does each perform, according to NAR prophet Bill Hamon? (See pp. 47-51.)

8. Review the list of specific things a NAR prophet does for individuals (see pp. 48-49). Has a "prophet" ever done any of these things for you? Describe the circumstances. How did this come about? What did the prophet say to you? Did the prophet support his or her claims with evidence you could assess? Did you agree with the prophecy? Were you pleased with the prophecy given to you? Did you harbor suspicions? Did the prophet claim that his or her word was certain? Or did he or she claim that it may be in error? What was your evaluation of the prophecy at the time? What is your overall evaluation now? Review chapter 5 and study chapters 6 and 7 of this book. Then evaluate this prophecy according to the principles described in this book.

9. What is a "prophetic presbytery"? What does this group do? (See footnote 6, p. 48.)

10. What types of NAR prophecies have been given for whole nations? Do you believe there are high-ranking demons that rule over nations? Is this a biblical concept? Are we to wage spiritual warfare against these demons? (See p. 49.)

11. What is the NAR teaching about prophets who reveal new truths for the entire church? (See pp. 50-51.) Why does Bill Hamon call these revelations "restored truths"? State as exactly as you can the idea of "the prophetic illumination of Scripture" (see p. 50). Is this a legitimate practice when interpreting the Bible? What dangers are there in using this principle? Do you know of anyone who has used this principle to interpret the Bible?

12. How do NAR leaders interpret Ephesians 3:4-5? Is this a responsible interpretation of the passage? (See pp. 50-51.)

13. What does Bill Hamon say about the difference between revelations given to an apostle and revelations given to a prophet? What is his basis for this claim? Does it seem plausible to you? Evaluate his claim. (See pp. 50-51.)

14. What new truths have been revealed to NAR prophets, according to NAR leaders? (See p. 51.)

15. What is the Apostolic Council of Prophetic Elders? Have you heard of any of the members listed in the book? What activities do they perform? Have you ever consulted their "Word of the Lord" revelations? What experiences have you had with any of the groups led by members of the Apostolic Council of Prophetic Elders? What is your own evaluation of their claims and activities? We suggest that you examine their practices using the guidelines developed in this book. (See pp. 45-46.)

16. What thoughts and questions do you have as a result of reading this chapter?

# Chapter 6

# Prophets in the Bible: A Close Look

1. Why have the prophets of the Old Testament been referred to as "covenant reinforcers"? (See p. 52.)

2. What is the significance of Deuteronomy 18:15? (See p. 53, including footnote 2.) What was the ultimate message of the Old Testament prophets? What verses support this claim?

3. Doug and Holly describe six broad "functions" typical of Old Testament prophets. What are these functions? Some prophets were organized into companies called "sons of the prophets." How are these prophets described in the Old Testament? (See pp. 54-55.)

4.  There were also New Testament prophets. Make a list of these figures. What is the central message of the New Testament prophets? What functions did they serve? (See pp. 56-58.)

5.  Doug and Holly briefly describe one function that was not performed by the New Testament prophets. What function is that? How does this differ from the way Old Testament prophets frequently functioned? (See pp. 58-59.)

6. Revelation 11:6 speaks of two witnesses who would prophesy. Who are these prophets? How are they related to the line of Old and New Testament prophets? What is significant about this for evaluating NAR claims about present-day prophets? (See pp. 58-59.)

7. Believers are warned about "false prophets," both in the Old Testament and in the New Testament. What do we learn about false prophets from the Old Testament? What do we learn from the New Testament? In the New Testament, believers are warned that some who prophesy will be effective deceivers; some will perform miracles. What warning is implied by these assertions? (See pp. 59-60.)

8. Doug and Holly call genuine prophets "prophets of God"; others are called "false prophets" (on p. 60). What is the point of this distinction?

9. What thoughts and questions do you have as a result of reading this chapter?

# Chapter 7

# NAR Prophets vs. Prophets in the Bible

1.  What is the major thesis of this chapter? (See p. 61 and p. 78.)

2. What do NAR leaders teach about the governing role of a prophet in the church today? What passages in the New Testament do they use to support their teaching? (See p. 47.) How do Doug and Holly reply to these understandings of the passages? (See pp. 29-31.)

3. What do NAR leaders teach about Amos 3:7? (See p. 47.) How do Doug and Holly reply to this understanding of the verse? (See p. 62.)

4. What is the New Testament evidence that prophets held governing roles in the early churches? (See p. 61.) What is the Old Testament evidence that prophets governed? (See pp. 61-62.)

5. How does the NAR view of prophets' authority go beyond more traditional views about the spiritual gift of prophecy? (See pp. 62-63.)

6. What is the New Testament evidence that prophets revealed individuals' spiritual gifts and ministries? Is there any evidence that New Testament prophets guided individuals in making major life decisions? What are the dangers of prophets giving such guidance to individuals? (See pp. 62-64.) Have you ever been given life direction by a prophet? Have you, or someone you've known, ever experienced harm from following guidance given by a prophet?

7. Why are many followers of NAR prophets afraid ever to question the teachings of NAR prophets? Have you, or someone you've known, ever been afraid to question the teachings of a NAR prophet? What does Scripture teach about testing prophecies and prophets? (See p. 70.)

8. Doug and Holly describe five tests for genuine prophets. What are these tests? Do you agree that these are biblically grounded tests for a prophet? Do you think there are other tests that should be used to evaluate a person's claim to be a prophet? (See pp. 70-77.)

9. In Doug and Holly's view, how have NAR leaders fallen short in applying the three key tests for prophets? (See pp. 70-77.) In your own observations, have these tests for a prophet been applied consistently in churches you've attended or by NAR organizations and leaders you've followed?

10. Do you know anyone who claims to be a prophet? Does that person meet all three tests for a genuine prophet? What would such a person say about the three tests for a prophet described by Doug and Holly in this chapter? Do you know anyone today who meets all three tests of a prophet?

11. Had you heard of the Passion Translation prior to reading this book? Do you know anyone who uses Brian Simmons' "translation"? Why the need for a new Bible translation, according to Simmons? What are some problems with Simmons' translation, according to Doug and Holly? What are marks of a trustworthy translation of the Bible? (See pp. 67-69.)

12. What thoughts and questions do you have as a result of reading this chapter?

# Chapter 8

# Strategic-Level Spiritual Warfare

1. Read the three true stories on pages 79-80. How did you feel about the actions of the people in these stories? What is the common purpose behind their actions? Have you, or someone you've known, ever engaged in similar actions?

2. What is strategic-level spiritual warfare? What NAR belief is strategic-level spiritual warfare based on? What is the Great End-Time Harvest and how is it related to NAR teaching about strategic-level spiritual warfare? (See p. 81.)

3. What have more traditional Christians taught about spiritual warfare? (See p. 81.)

4. How is strategic-level spiritual warfare related to NAR teachings about advancing God's kingdom? How do NAR methods
to advance God's kingdom differ from methods used by more
traditional Christians? (See p. 81.)

5. According to NAR teachers, who must take the lead in waging
strategic-level spiritual warfare and why? (See p. 82.)

6. What are the key Bible passages used by NAR teachers to support their teachings about strategic-level spiritual warfare? How do they understand these passages? (See pp. 82-84.)

7. What is spiritual mapping and what is the purpose of this practice? Which book popularized spiritual mapping and who wrote this book? Name a well-known mission organization that has practiced spiritual mapping. (See pp. 84-86.) Have you, or someone you've known, ever been involved in a spiritual mapping project? What were the results?

8. What is prayerwalking and what is the purpose of this practice? (See p. 86.) What Old Testament story is an example of a prayerwalk, according to NAR leaders? Have you, or someone you've known, ever undertaken a prayerwalk? Were you aware of the NAR teachings that often lie behind this practice?

9. What is the Seven Mountain Mandate and how does it relate to strategic-level spiritual warfare? What seven societal institutions are targeted by this mandate? Who alone has the authority to rise to the top of these institutions? (See pp. 87-88.) Have you personally encountered teaching about the Seven Mountain Mandate?

10. What is the Great End-Time Transfer of Wealth and how is it related to the Seven Mountain Mandate? (See p. 87.)

11. How did Frank Peretti's novel *This Present Darkness* popularize NAR practices of strategic-level spiritual warfare? (See p. 83.) Did you ever read this novel? What did you think about it at the time and have your views changed since then?

12. Review the list of organizations engaged in strategic-level spiritual warfare, found on pages 89 and 90. Have you heard of these organizations? Were you surprised by any organizations included in this list? Do you know of any other organizations that engage in practices of strategic-level spiritual warfare?

13. What thoughts and questions do you have as a result of reading this chapter?

# Chapter 9

# What the Bible Really Teaches About Spiritual Warfare

1.  Is there any biblical evidence that territorial spirits exist? (See p. 91.)

2.  Is there any biblical support for the NAR teaching that territo-
    rial spirits must be cast out before the gospel can go forth and
    God's kingdom can advance? How do Doug and Holly reply to
    the NAR claim that the biblical prophet Daniel engaged in stra-
    tegic-level spiritual warfare? How do Doug and Holly reply to
    C. Peter Wagner's understanding of Ephesians 3:10? (See pp.
    91-92.)

3.  Is there any indication in the Bible that Christians have been
    authorized to cast out demons from individuals? (See p. 92.)

4. What New Testament passages indicate that directly confronting territorial spirits may actually be dangerous? (See p. 92 and read these passages.)

5. How do Doug and Holly answer the question, "Is spiritual mapping biblical?" Are there any types of spiritual mapping projects that may be biblical? (See pp. 92-93.)

6. What New Testament verse contradicts the NAR teaching that knowing the name of a demon gives Christians more control over that demon? (See pp. 92-93.)

7. Is there biblical support for prayerwalks that involve attempts to directly confront territorial spirits? How do Doug and Holly reply to the NAR claim that the Israelites' march around Jericho is an example of a NAR-type prayerwalk? (See pp. 93-94.)

8. Are there any types of prayerwalks that may be biblical? Have you ever participated in such a prayerwalk or do you know others who have? Why do Doug and Holly suggest that "prayerwalking" might not be the best term for this practice? (See p. 94.)

9. Is there biblical support for the NAR teaching that territorial spirits must be cast out of societal institutions? How about the NAR teaching that apostles have divine authority to govern societal institutions? Did New Testament apostles have authority to govern beyond the church? (See p. 94.)

10. If you've encountered the Seven Mountain Mandate teaching, did you, at that time, realize that it limits the most impactful ministry to NAR apostles? (See p. 95.) If so, how did you feel about that teaching then? How do you feel about it now?

11. What thoughts and questions do you have as a result of reading this chapter?

# Chapter 10

# Unifying the Forces Through Apostolic Unity

1. What is meant by "apostolic unity"? Why is there a need for apostolic unity, according to NAR leaders? (See p. 96.)

2. Have you heard of the Call assemblies? What is the purpose of these assemblies? What is the premise behind these assemblies? (See p. 96.) Do you know anyone who has attended one of these assemblies? Were they aware of its association with the NAR movement?

3. What is an example of a city that has experienced transformation under an apostle's leadership, according to NAR leaders? How do they claim this city was transformed? (See pp. 96-97.)

4. Why hasn't the church yet achieved unity, according to NAR leaders? (See p. 98.)

5. What are some differences between "apostolic unity" and "doctrinal unity"? What classically orthodox Christian doctrine is denied by some groups that NAR leaders have agreed to partner with? (See pp. 98-99.)

6. What key Bible passage is used to support NAR teaching on apostolic unity? What is the NAR understanding of this passage? (See p. 99.)

7. Which New Testament passages teach the importance of Christian unity? According to the apostle Paul, what was the foundation of the unity among the churches in Asia Minor? Read Ephesians 4:11-13. How does this passage show that the foundation of Christian unity is a shared commitment to fundamental beliefs? (See pp. 99-100.)

8. Is apostolic unity in the NAR sense promoted anywhere in the New Testament? What was the result when the Corinthians rallied around certain church leaders? (See pp. 100-101.)

9. Can Christians from different denominations ever work together, in Doug and Holly's view? What, in their view, should be the dividing line when deciding whom to partner with? (See p. 101.) Do you agree with them? What do you think the dividing line should be?

10. What thoughts and questions do you have as a result of reading this chapter?

# Chapter 11

# A Miracle-Working Army

1. Review Mike, Vickie, and Marie's stories. (See pp. 102-103.) What do they share in common?

2. Do any biblically orthodox Christians believe that miracles play a role in the church today? Do you believe miracles play a role in the church today? What sets more traditional Christian beliefs about miracles apart from the radical beliefs of people in NAR? (See pp. 103-104 and the summary on p. 114.)

3. What are some ways people in NAR seek to learn to work miracles? (See p. 104.) What do you think about the NAR teaching that you can learn to work miracles? Have you ever read a book or received training designed to teach you to prophesy or develop other miraculous powers? What was involved with the training? What were the results?

4. In your own words, what is a Treasure Hunt? (See p. 105.) Do you know anyone who has engaged in a Treasure Hunt, a.k.a. "supernatural evangelism" or "prophetic evangelism"? If so, share what you know about their experiences with this type of evangelism.

5. What are some ways children in NAR are trained to work miracles? (See pp. 105-106.)

6. How do some individuals in NAR seek to overcome sickness and death? Which influential NAR leader teaches that elderly followers of NAR apostles and prophets will experience a reverse aging process, growing physically younger? (See p. 106.)

7. Which influential NAR leader teaches that Christians can become immortal through the reception of new truths being given by NAR apostles and prophets? Do all NAR leaders agree with this teaching? Why do Doug and Holly feel it is important to address this teaching? Name some influential NAR leaders who have endorsed Hamon's books that promote this teaching? (See p. 108.)

8. How will people in NAR execute the judgments of God on earth? (See p. 108.) Which influential NAR leader, identified in this book, teaches that the end-time church will loose God's judgments on earth before Christ returns? How does NAR teaching about the book of Revelation differ from more traditional interpretations of the book of Revelation? (See pp. 109-110.)

9. What does all miracle-working power promised to NAR followers depend on? (See p. 110.)

10. What is the NAR understanding of John 14:12? How does 2 Kings 6:1-2 support the NAR practice of establishing supernatural schools of ministry, according to NAR leaders? What is the NAR understanding of Romans 8:19-23 and what is the name of this particular NAR teaching? Which verse in the preceding passage teaches that the followers of NAR apostles and prophets will overcome death, according to Bill Hamon? What specific language is often used to describe the NAR teaching about people in NAR becoming a type of corporate Christ? (See pp. 111-112.)

11. List some NAR practices that are new truths revealed by NAR apostles and prophets so people can learn to work miracles. (See pp. 112-114.) Were you surprised by any of these practices? If so, why? On page 114, Doug and Holly note that some of these practices, such as fasting and speaking in tongues, are also practiced by Christians who are not part of NAR. Does your church promote any of the practices listed on pages 112-114? If so, are they viewed as keys for learning to work miracles or are they viewed differently? Have you taken part in any of these practices? If so, did you see them as keys for learning to work miracles or did you view them differently?

12. What thoughts and questions do you have as a result of reading this chapter?

# Chapter 12

# What the Bible Really Teaches About Miracles

1. Review the NAR understanding of John 14:12. (See p. 110.) How do Doug and Holly reply to this NAR understanding of the passage? (See pp. 115-117.) In their view, what are the "greater works" Jesus spoke of?

2. Which two Scripture passages written by the apostle Paul do Doug and Holly cite to refute the NAR teaching that people can learn to work miracles? (See p. 118.) Read these passages.

3. Review the NAR understanding of 1 Kings 6:1-2. (See pp. 110-111.) Do the "schools of the prophets" found in the Old Testament give support for NAR schools of supernatural ministry? (See pp. 118-119.)

4. What does NAR teaching about "activating" miraculous gifts in individuals share in common with New Age teachings? (See pp. 118-119.)

5. Doug and Holly agree that fasting and prayer are biblical practices. So what do they find problematic about Mike Bickle's Global Bridegroom Fast and his teaching about 24/7 prayer rooms? (See pp. 119-121.)

6. Review the NAR understanding of Romans 8:19-23, specifically in relation to NAR teaching about overcoming sickness and death. (See pp. 111-112.) Doug and Holly argue that this NAR interpretation of the passage is "faulty." (See p. 122.) What, in their view, is the correct understanding of the passage?

7. How do Doug and Holly reply to Bill Hamon's teaching that the church is a type of corporate Christ? (See p. 122.) What is meant when the New Testament refers to the church as "Christ's body" (and what is not meant)? In what way do Christians become "partakers of the divine nature"? (See 2 Peter 1:4.)

8. Why do Doug and Holly write that "there remains some mystery about his [Mike Bickle's] perspective on Manifest Sons of God teaching"? (See p. 123.) Do you agree?

9. In contrast to Bickle's view that the end-time church will loose God's judgments on earth prior to Christ's return, what are the views of biblical scholars? If the church will indeed join Christ in executing judgment, as some scholars believe, why is the question of timing crucial? (See pp. 123-124.) Why is Bickle's teaching about Christians loosing judgments on unbelievers a "terrible truth"? (See p. 124.)

10. Had you heard of the Dead Raising Team prior to reading this book? (See p. 107.) What are your thoughts about this organization's activities? Do you believe their claim to have seen eleven resurrections? If not, what sort of evidence would you require before believing their claim?

11. What thoughts and questions do you have as a result of reading this chapter?

# Conclusion

1. What did Doug and Holly aim to do when they wrote this book? (See p. 125.) Do you think they succeeded in their aim?

2. What is the core NAR teaching, in Doug and Holly's view? What is the NAR rationale for this teaching? (See p. 125.) After reading this book, do you agree with the authors' conclusion that the "Bible does not support these claims"?

3. What example of one false belief did Doug and Holly suggest might not be as harmful as other false beliefs? (See p. 126.) Can you think of other examples of false beliefs that may not ultimately be very harmful?

4. List and briefly explain four dangers that are posed by NAR teachings, according to Doug and Holly. (See pp. 126-128.) Have you, or someone you've known, ever experienced any of these dangers as a result of NAR teachings? Would you add any other dangers to their list?

5. What thoughts and questions do you have as a result of reading the conclusion to *God's Super-Apostles*?

6. What new information have you learned from this book? How will you respond? Has it given you any ideas for further study?

7. Did this book impact you personally in any way? Did it challenge any of your beliefs?

8. Do you have any other thoughts, or action plans, as a result of reading this book?

9. Do you know anyone else who would benefit from reading this book?

# Appendix A

# Advice for Parents, Pastors, and Participants in the New Apostolic Reformation

1. According to Doug and Holly, if a parent is concerned that a child has embraced NAR beliefs, the first step a parent should take is to clarify what the child actually believes. Why is this important, and what are some tips they give for clarifying a child's beliefs? (See pp. 129-130.)

2. The second step a parent should take, according to Doug and Holly, is to gently challenge a child to support any questionable NAR beliefs from Scripture. What are some recommendations they give for challenging a child with Scripture? (See pp. 130-131.) Have you already been doing any of these things with your own children? Are any of these recommendations new to you? Do you plan to adopt any of them?

3. In talking with your child, why is it crucial that you conduct yourself with kindness and gentleness? (See pp. 131-132 and 1 Peter 3:15-16.)

4. What word of encouragement do Doug and Holly give to parents of young children? (See p. 132.) This encouragement can also apply to grandparents, Sunday school teachers, and any others who have influence in the lives of young children. What specific ways can you use your influence to teach children to test every teaching against Scripture?

5. What recommendations do Doug and Holly give to pastors, church leaders, and anyone else who has a teaching platform in a church? (See pp. 133-134.) Do you have a teaching platform? If so, what are some ways you can you use your platform to educate and warn people about NAR?

6. What five recommendations do Doug and Holly give to some-one who has been involved in NAR and wants to separate from this movement? (See pp. 134-136.) If you've been involved in NAR, which of these recommendations do you find most help-ful? Which would be most difficult?

# Appendix B

# Questions to Ask of Churches

1. If you want to know if a church or organization is associated with NAR, why is it important to look beyond their statement of faith? Why wouldn't it help much if all you do is ask if they're affiliated with NAR? (See p. 137.)

2.  What are some terms that might provide clues that a church is associated with NAR? (See p. 137.) What other terms might you add to this list? Have you encountered any of these terms being used in your church?

3.  How can a church's promotion of certain books provide useful clues? (See p. 137.) Have you seen any books written by NAR leaders being promoted in your church?

4. Briefly review the list of questions you can ask church leaders to help you find out where they stand on NAR teachings. (See pp. 138-139.) Have you ever asked your church leaders these questions? Do you think they would welcome your questions?

5. Do you know of any individuals in your church who hold NAR views? If so, have you asked these individuals specifically how they learned about these things? Have you asked how their views have been received by other people in the church, including its leaders? (See p. 139.)

6. If you don't know where your church stands on NAR issues, do you plan to find out? If so, what is your action plan?

# Appendix C

# Name-Calling

1. What do Doug and Holly mean when they refer to the practice of "name-calling"? What is one harmful effect of this practice? (See p. 140.)

2. Why should you not be afraid to challenge the claims of a NAR apostle or prophet? (See p. 140.) Have you ever been afraid to challenge an apostle or prophet (or any other church leader)? If so, why? Do you feel this way now?

3. Briefly review the list of nine insulting names often applied to those who challenge NAR apostles and prophets (on pp. 140-141). Have you ever been called any of these names? Have you been called any other insulting names for challenging an apostle or prophet (or other church leader)? If so, how did that make you feel? Have you ever been reluctant to challenge an apostle or prophet out of fear of being labeled with an insulting name?

# Another resource on the New Apostolic Reformation

'An eye-opening
exposé of a
rapidly growing
phenomenon'

Daniel B. Wallace,
Dallas Theological
Seminary

'All who care for the
health of the church
need to read this
book.'

Craig A. Evans,
Houston Baptist University

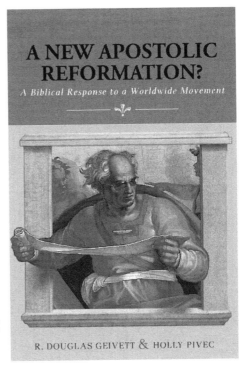

**A NEW APOSTOLIC REFORMATION?**
*A Biblical Response to a Worldwide Movement*

R. DOUGLAS GEIVETT & HOLLY PIVEC

This volume, also written by Doug and Holly, is a more extensive treatment of the New Apostolic Reformation. It expands on the documentation and analysis provided in *God's Super-Apostles*.

*A New Apostolic Reformation?:*
*A Biblical Response to a Worldwide Movement*
By R. Douglas Geivett and Holly Pivec
Weaver Book Company

***Available in stores and online!***

If you found this study guide helpful, please consider writing a review on Amazon.

Made in the USA
Columbia, SC
24 March 2021